# Barbie ™

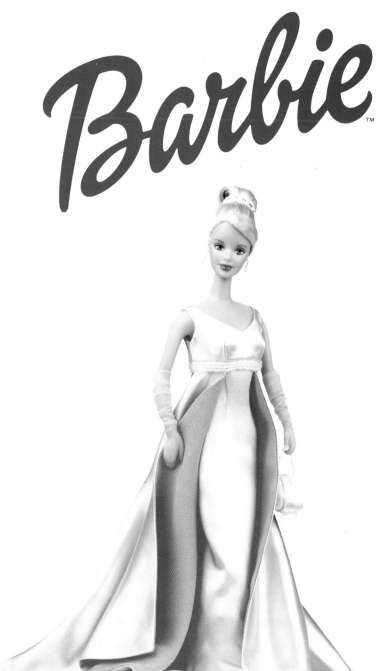

## FASHION DOLLS
# STICKER BOOK

A Dorling Kindersley Book

# Spring and summer

Fashion designers are people who come up with new ideas for clothes. Each year, they hold two shows so people can see the new looks. Models parade the spring and summer outfits at one show, and wear the autumn and winter styles at the other. Here's Barbie in some favourite spring and summer looks.

**Ready for the sun**
Once, only bicyclists wore trousers like these – that's why they are called pedal pushers. Today, they are a summer fashion favourite.

**Slumber party**
The perfect outfit for a summer sleepover. Teddies are invited, too!

Super sunhat

Cool sunglasses

**Tennis dress**
In the early 20th century, ladies wore ankle-length dresses to play tennis!

Sunshine yellow

Picnic basket

**At the beach**
Barbie is ready for the sun in a bikini top and matching skirt. Many people were shocked when bikinis appeared in the 1940s, but now you see lots of these cute two-piece outfits at the beach.

**Just jeans**
Denim jeans are a family fashion classic. Your parents probably own a pair – and your grandparents too! Barbie looks funky in wide-legged jeans and a lilac top.

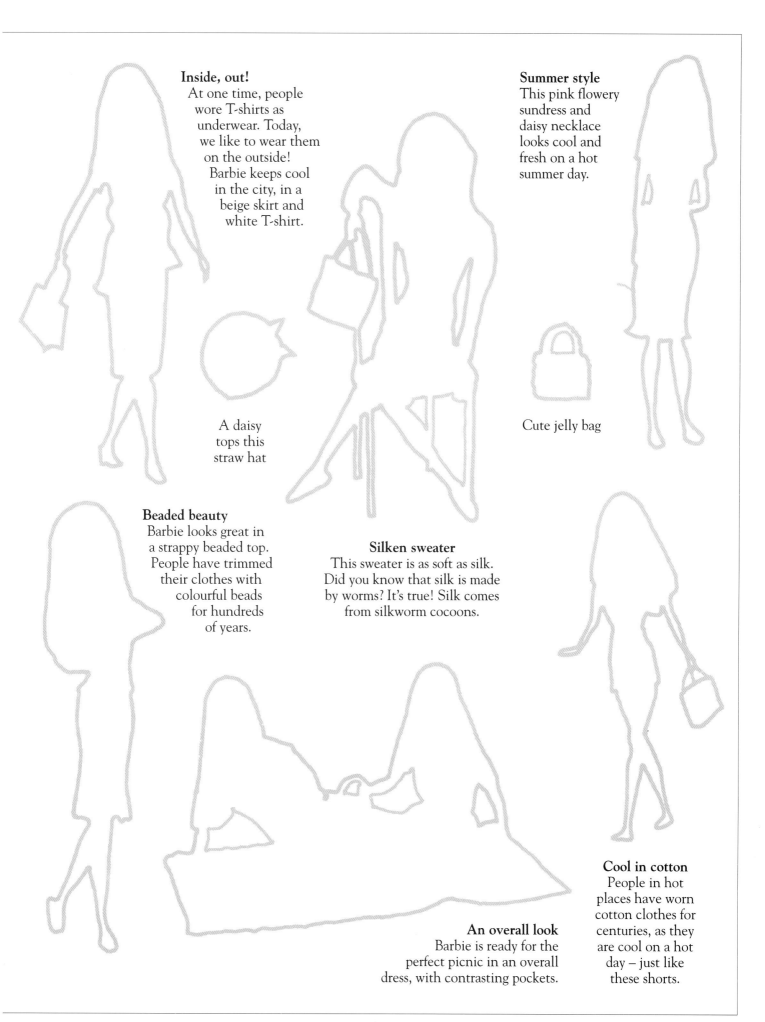

**Inside, out!**
At one time, people wore T-shirts as underwear. Today, we like to wear them on the outside! Barbie keeps cool in the city, in a beige skirt and white T-shirt.

A daisy tops this straw hat

**Summer style**
This pink flowery sundress and daisy necklace looks cool and fresh on a hot summer day.

Cute jelly bag

**Beaded beauty**
Barbie looks great in a strappy beaded top. People have trimmed their clothes with colourful beads for hundreds of years.

**Silken sweater**
This sweater is as soft as silk. Did you know that silk is made by worms? It's true! Silk comes from silkworm cocoons.

**An overall look**
Barbie is ready for the perfect picnic in an overall dress, with contrasting pockets.

**Cool in cotton**
People in hot places have worn cotton clothes for centuries, as they are cool on a hot day – just like these shorts.

# Autumn and winter

The leaves are falling from the trees and the temperature has dropped outside. It's time for Barbie to put away her spring and summer wardrobe and try on some of the new looks for autumn and winter – cosy coats, brilliant boots, and wonderful woollies!

**Trendy trousers**
In Europe and North America, only men wore trousers until the 1900s. Now no girl would be without them.

Silver duffel bag

**Quick change!**
Looping a jumper loosely around your waist looks great, and it is very practical too. When it gets cold, slip it on and you have a whole new look!

Cosy purple fleece

**Mini miss**
Mini skirts were made popular in 1967, by a designer called Mary Quant. They are still worn today, but they were a lot shorter in the 1960s!

**Classic colours**
Black and white is a classic colour choice. It always looks stylish and smart. This outfit is spiced up by a colourful top.

**Winter wonderland**
Barbie is ready to brave the cold in a fluffy pink and white jumper with a matching fluffy bag. Silver gloves and boots complete her outfit.

# FASHION BARBIE

Pink gown with hooped skirt

Fleecy top

Flower girl

Classic white T-shirt

Satin wedding gown

Winter boots

Mint-green summer ball gown

Tennis dress

Skirts and boots

# FASHION BARBIE

Faux fur bag

Coat with faux
fur trim

Full-skirted dress with lace bodice

Knitted
bikini

Wedding gift

Classic combination

Pink empire line gown

Chiffon
scarf

Sunglasses

Fluffy pink jumper and bag

Overall dresses

# FASHION BARBIE

Cosy ski jacket

Picnic basket

Straw hat

Evening bag

Black boots

Elegant skirt and top

Shortie pyjama set

Glamorous, film star gown

Romantic wedding gown

Umbrella

Silver jeans

# FASHION BARBIE

Summery beaded top

Parka

Lavender dress with sparkling "diamonds"

Beautiful bride

Jelly bag

Necklace

Cotton shorts

Flowery sundress

Taffeta dress and wrap

Barbie in boots

# FASHION BARBIE

Duffel
bag

Pearls

Jersey dress

Soft as
silk

Bridesmaid's dress

Wedding
cake

Green dress
and diamond
necklace

Ear muffs

Smart
trousers

Bikini top

# FASHION BARBIE

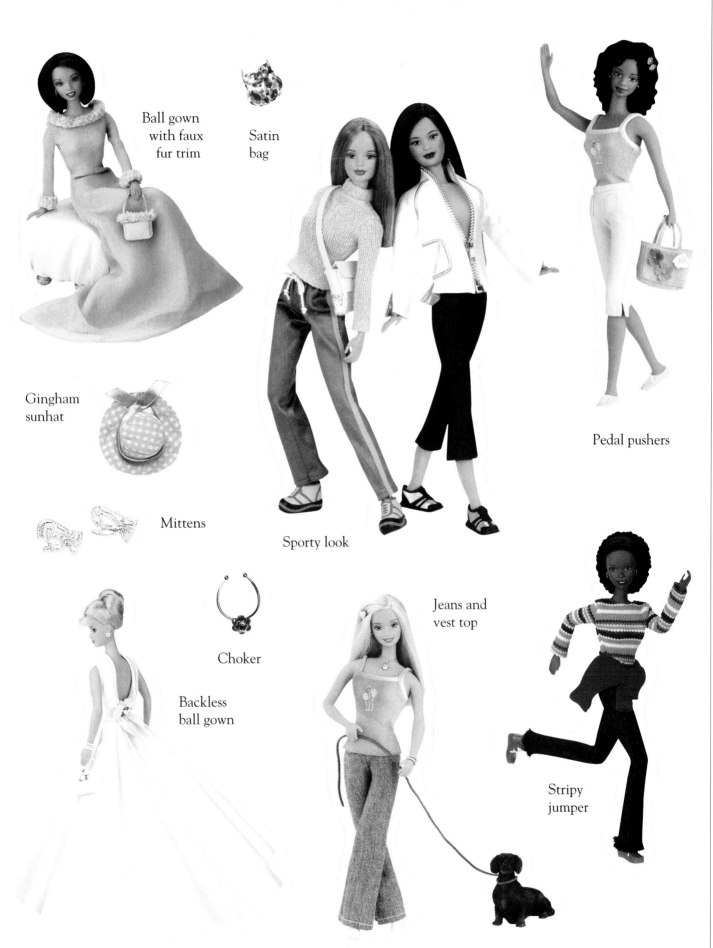

Ball gown
with faux
fur trim

Satin
bag

Gingham
sunhat

Mittens

Sporty look

Pedal pushers

Choker

Jeans and
vest top

Backless
ball gown

Stripy
jumper

**Space girl**
After astronauts flew
into space in the
1960s, designers
began to make
clothes from
silver, "space age"
fabrics. These
silver jeans are
definitely "out
of this world!"

Ice-blue parka

**Evening out**
This purple jersey
dress is perfect for
an evening out.
The pattern on
the dress matches
the bag exactly.

Winter
footwear

Earmuffs

Funky,
faux
fur bag

Keep
dry in
the rain!

**Sports style**
Once, people only wore tracksuits and trainers
to exercise classes, or the playing field. Now, sports
fashion inspires some of the coolest outfits around.

**Boot-i-ful Barbie!**
Barbie looks great
in these suede boots.
Did you know that
the first pair of ladies'
boots were truly
"fit for a queen"?
They were made for
British ruler Queen
Victoria, in 1840.

Smart black boots

Yellow vinyl
coat, trimmed
with faux fur

**Ski sensation**
Barbie's ski jacket is made
from a special windproof
and waterproof material –
essential for keeping warm
and dry on the slopes.

5

# Something special

Whether it is spring or autumn, everyone looks forward to seeing the evening dresses at a fashion show! These romantic, glamorous gowns are truly special. It's a chance for the designer to bring a little fairytale magic to everybody's day!

**Summer dance**
With its pastel flowers and little straps, this mint-green dress has a summery feel – perfect for waltzing on warm evenings.

Rose-detail choker

**Glittering gown**
Every girl will shine in this gorgeous dress. The top is covered in sparkling stones which twinkle like stars when they catch the light!

Satin evening bag

**Elegant empire**
This dress has a high waistband and a long, straight skirt. It's in a style called empire line, which began in the 19th century – but still looks great today!

**Faux fur is fun!**
Faux fur like this first appeared in the 1960s.

**Delicate diamond**
Barbie wears a diamond pendant necklace. Diamonds are valued in 'carats'. The higher the carat, the more valuable the diamond.

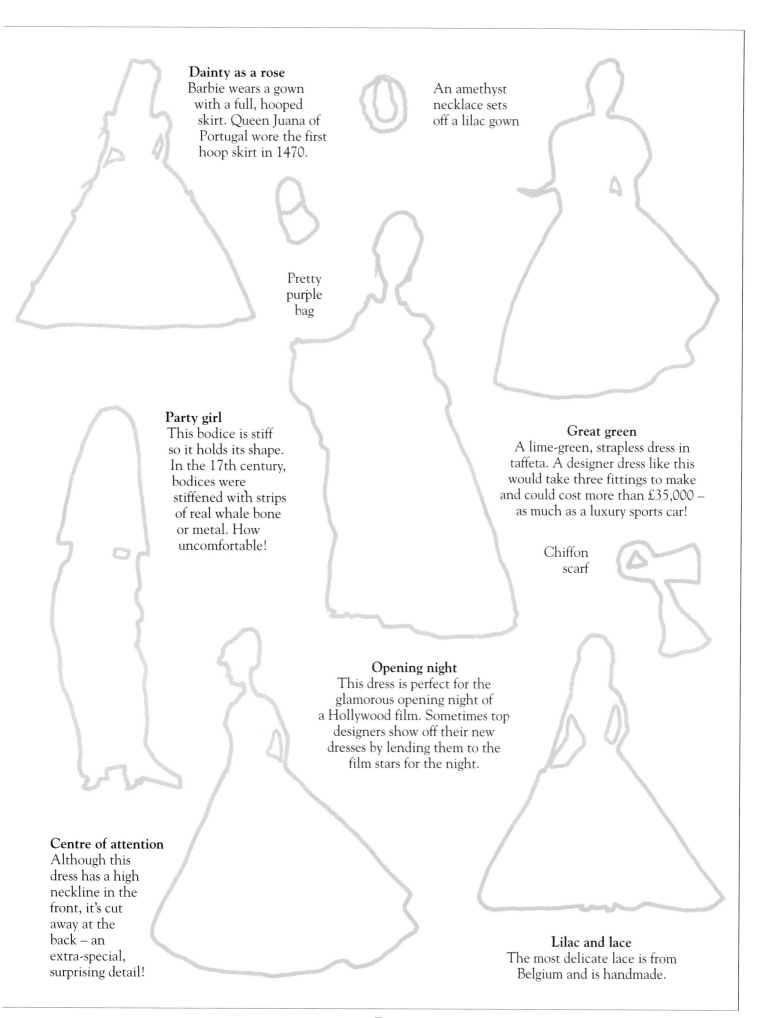

**Dainty as a rose**
Barbie wears a gown with a full, hooped skirt. Queen Juana of Portugal wore the first hoop skirt in 1470.

An amethyst necklace sets off a lilac gown

Pretty purple bag

**Party girl**
This bodice is stiff so it holds its shape. In the 17th century, bodices were stiffened with strips of real whale bone or metal. How uncomfortable!

**Great green**
A lime-green, strapless dress in taffeta. A designer dress like this would take three fittings to make and could cost more than £35,000 – as much as a luxury sports car!

Chiffon scarf

**Opening night**
This dress is perfect for the glamorous opening night of a Hollywood film. Sometimes top designers show off their new dresses by lending them to the film stars for the night.

**Centre of attention**
Although this dress has a high neckline in the front, it's cut away at the back – an extra-special, surprising detail!

**Lilac and lace**
The most delicate lace is from Belgium and is handmade.

# Wedding dresses

Fashion shows often end in a spectacular way,
with a beautiful model wearing wedding dress designs.
Designers often pick their favourite model to wear the
dress – so it is an honour to be chosen! Here's Barbie,
modelling some traditional wedding dresses.

**Blushing bride**
White became popular
for wedding dresses in
the 16th century.
Before then, the
bride simply wore
her best dress,
of any colour.

String of
pearls

**Wedding belles**
The first bridal veils were yellow,
and they weren't see-through at
all – the bride could not see out
and the groom could not see in!

Cutting the
cake is a special
part of the
wedding day

People give the
wedding couple
gifts – usually
something for
the home

**Day to remember**
Barbie looks
radiant in this
satin gown,
trimmed with
pearls. Satin has
a wonderful
sheen and is
perfect for a
wedding dress.

**Bright bouquet**
Bridal flowers hold
special meanings.
For example,
beautiful roses
are a symbol
of true love.

**Beautiful bridesmaid**
A bridesmaid gives the bride
a helping hand. Perhaps she will
hold the flowers during the
ceremony, or carry the veil.